This book
belongs to:

....

This edition first published in 2015 by Milly&Flynn®
an imprint of Ginger Fox Ltd
Stirling House, College Road, Cheltenham GL53 7HY
United Kingdom

www.millyandflynn.com
www.gingerfox.co.uk

Copyright © 2015 Ginger Fox Ltd

Written by Moira Butterfield
Illustrated by Michael Emmerson

ISBN: 978-1-909290-79-2

10 9 8 7 6 5 4 3 2 1

Printed and bound in China

I saw a SHARK!

I went to the park and I saw ...

I went to the park and I saw ...

I went to the park
and I saw ...

I went to the park and I saw ...

I went to the park and I saw ...

I went to the park and I saw ...

I went to the park and I saw ...

I went to the park and I saw ...

...r
on
m:
dro,"
tro.

... ten fairies riding silver snails,
catching mice by their wriggly tails.

I went to the park and I saw ...

3 dragons

4 tigers

7 mermaids

8 rats

1 shark

2 witches

5 elephants

6 ghosties

9 genies

10 fairies